# Brown Hands, Black HBCUs

## By Latoya Turner

### Illustrated by Cameron Leost

To current HBCU students and alumni, be sure to teach our youth about HBCUs.

# I pledge to learn about HBCUs.

_____

Name

It was the night before the first day of school. Aria and Walter packed their backpack in order to be prepared for school.

In the morning, Aria woke up and went into Walter's room and began singing, "It's the first day of school; it's the first day of school; I CAN'T WAAAAIT, it's the first day of school!" Aria and Walter got ready, and their dad drove them to school. Once they arrived, they walked to their classroom. A tall, pretty lady greeted Aria at the door with a smile and said, "Hi, I'm Mrs. Phelps, your teacher. What's your name?" "Aria," she replied.

During school, the class learned different things, sang songs, and danced. "Class, you are going to think of a creative way to share about a time you went on an adventure. You will work on this at home," said Mrs. Phelps.

After school, Mom picked up Aria and Walter. "How was your first day of school?" Mom asked. "I loved it, my teacher is nice, and she let us dance, but I have homework to do," sighed Aria. Walter laughed and said, "It was cool. I saw some friends from last school year."

Later that day at home, Aria read a note from her teacher to her parents.

Share about a time you went on an adventure. Be creative. Due this Friday!

"That should be fun. You should share about the time that we went to Turks and Caicos," said Dad. "I already told my friends about Turks," said Aria! "Share about the time you and Walter went to visit your cousin Maya's HBCU Central State University for homecoming," said Mom. Aria jumped up with excitement and imagined being there. "That's it, thanks, Mom," said Aria excitedly.

Every day after school, Aria worked on her project with the help of her family. Aria worked hard and couldn't wait to share her adventure with her classmates.

It was Friday and time for everyone to share their adventure. "Well, boys and girls, it's time to present," said Mrs. Phelps. Aria's friend Norah raised her hand to go first. "You may present," said Mrs. Phelps. Norah showed the class her souvenirs from when she visited her family in the Bahamas. Norah also taught the class about her Caribbean culture. Afterwards, the class cheered for Norah. It was then Aria's turn to present. Aria proudly walked to the front of the classroom.

"Last summer, my brother Walter and I visited my cousin Maya's HBCU for homecoming. She attends Central State University in Wilberforce, Ohio. HBCU stands for Historically Black Colleges and Universities. CSU was founded in 1887. It is located in a rural community, and their school colors are maroon and gold. Their mascot is a marauder, a pirate! CSU prepares students with diverse backgrounds and experiences for the world. You can study there and become a teacher, like Mrs. Phelps," said Aria.

**Marauders !**

Aria continued. "We walked on the yard through the Sunken Garden, ate good food, and watched the football game. The fraternities and sororities stepped at the step show, like the Alphas, Kappas, AKAs, and Deltas. I even saw the Invincible Marching Marauders Band! They played some of my favorite songs while my brother and I danced to the beat of the drums. Afterwards, we drove to town and stayed the night at Maya's apartment. She said her friends are like family, and one day I can go to an HBCU."

Once Aria was done presenting, the class clapped. "Great job Aria," shouted her classmates. Mrs. Phelps said, "I graduated from Alabama A&M University! It's an HBCU too. Thank you, Aria, for sharing your adventure with the class." Aria's face lit up! "Ok, boys and girls, choose a partner to research HBCUs, then I'll teach you what I know," said Mrs. Phelps. "Can we work on it outside?" Asked Norah. "Sure," said Mrs. Phelps.

Once they returned to the classroom, Mrs. Phelps said, "There are a little over 100 HBCUs in the U.S. In the past, African Americans could not attend colleges due to segregation. HBCUs gave Black people a chance to go to college to get an education and earn a degree. African Americans felt safe, happy, and welcomed at HBCUs. Students studied to become doctors, lawyers, and so much more. Each HBCU is special in its own way. If you ever go to an HBCU, always rep your school," said Mrs. Phelps. She then showed the class YouTube videos about the history of HBCUs.

Aria was so inspired by her teacher, but Mrs. Phelps was inspired by Aria even more. "You're never too young to learn about HBCUs; after all, HBCUs are a huge part of Black history. Black history should not only be celebrated in February; Black history should be celebrated every day," said Mrs. Phelps.

CELEBRATE

BLACK

HISTORY ~~MONTH~~

After school, Aria marched to her mom's car as if she was in a marching band at an HBCU. Mrs. Phelps marched beside her to let Aria's mom know that she had done a great job. Even though Aria was in elementary school, she already knew she wanted to attend an HBCU. When Aria got home, she shared what she had learned about HBCUs with her family. They were proud! "Good job, sis," said Walter. Aria smiled.

The following Monday at school, Mrs. Phelps said, "Open your hand." Mrs. Phelps placed a key in Aria's little brown hand. "Aria, let this key be a memory of when you first knew you wanted to attend an HBCU. You have the key to open any door. Continue to work hard and always believe in yourself," said Mrs. Phelps.

After school, Aria and Walter did their homework, the family ate dinner, and Aria and Walter went to bed that night, knowing that adventures allow you to see the world. When you see the world, you learn new things. And when you go to an HBCU, you can become anything you want. HBCUs celebrates the richness of African Americans. You can celebrate too, and have the time of your life! Just attend an HBCU after high school! Your brown hands will shine bright at any school, but more at a black school, like an HBCU! They were built for you! 🖤

# <u>Brown Hands, Black Schools Poem</u>

Brown Hands,

Black Schools,

HBCUs are cool.

Black and brown boys and girls,

Can go to college and feel joy.

ALL are welcome, can't you see,

That's right, even me.

Study, learn, and have fun,

Don't give up, get it done.

At HBCUs, we rep our school,

For me,  it's _____ (CSU).

- Latoya Turner

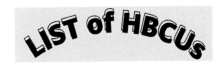

# LIST of HBCUs

## Alabama
Alabama A&M University

Alabama State University

Bishop State Community College

Gadsden State Community College

J. F. Drake State Community &

Technical College

Lawson State Community College

Miles College

Oakwood University

Selma University

Shelton State Community College

Stillman College

Talladega College

Trenholm State Community College

Tuskegee University

## Arkansas
Arkansas Baptist College

Philander Smith College

Shorter College

University of Arkansas at Pine Bluff

## California
Charles Drew University of Medicine

and Science

## Deleware
Delaware State University District of

Columbia

## Washington DC
Howard University

University of the District of Columbia

## Florida
Bethune - Cookman University

Edward Waters College

Florida A&M University

Florida Memorial University

## Georgia
Albany State University

Clark Atlanta University

Fort Valley State University

Interdenominational Theological Center

Morehouse College

Morehouse School of Medicine

Morris Brown College

Paine College

Savannah State University

Spelman College

## Kentucky

Kentucky State University

Simmons College

## Louisiana

Dillard University

Grambling State University

Southern University and A&M College

Southern University at New Orleans

Southern University at Shreveport

Southern University Law Center

Xavier University of Louisiana

## Maryland

Bowie State University

Coppin State University

Morgan State University

University of Maryland Eastern Shore

## Michigan

Pensole Lewis College of Business
and Design

## Mississippi

Alcon State University

Coahoma Community College

Jackson State University

Hinds Community College

Mississippi Valley State University

Rust College

Tougaloo College

## Missouri

Harris-Stowe State University

Lincoln University

## North Carolina

Bennett College

Elizabeth City Sate University

Fayetteville State University

Johnson C. Smith University

Livingstone College

North Carolina Central University

St. Augustine's University

Shaw University

Winston-Salem State University

## Ohio

Central State University

Wilberforce University

## Oklahoma

Langston University

## Pennsylvania

Cheyney University of Pennsylvania-**The
1st HBCU**

Lincoln University

## South Carolina

Allen University

Benedict College

Claflin University

Clinton College

Denmark Technical College

Morris College

South Carolina State University

Voorhees College

## Tennessee

American Baptist College

Fisk University

Lane College

LeMoyne-Owen College

Meharry Medical College

Tennessee State University

## Texas

Huston-Tillotson University

Jarvis Christian College

Langston University

Paul Quinn

Prairie View A&M University

Southwestern Christian College

St. Philip's College

Texas College

Texas Southern University

Wiley College

## United States Virgin Islands
University of the Virgin Islands

## Virginia
Hampton University
Norfolk State University
Virginia State University
Virginia Union University
Virginia University of Lynchburg

## West Virginia
Bluefield State College
West Virginia State University

# Guess what? They all attended an HBCU!

**Dr. Martin Luther King Jr.**
**Morehouse College**

**Oprah Winfrey**
**Tennessee State University**

**Kamala Harris**
**Howard University**

**Chadwick Boseman**
**Howard University**

**Michael Strahan**
**Texas Southern University**

# BROWN HANDS

Class of 2009

Latoya Turner is a primary educator. She is from Detroit, MI. She has taught grades K-2 with a little over 10 years of teaching experience. Latoya graduated from Central State University with a bachelor's degree in Early Childhood Education. She also graduated from Central Michigan University with a masters degree in Reading and Literacy. Latoya's goal is to educate all children about HBCUs.

**Check out Brown Hands, White Sand!**

**To connect with the author visit www.brownhandsllc.com**

**Follow us on social media @brownhandsllc**

**Thank You!**

Made in the USA
Columbia, SC
27 January 2023